Reader's Digest # READING
SKILL BUILDER

SILVER EDITION EDITORS

Miriam Weiss Meyer and Peter Travers, Project Editors

Barbara Antonopulos and Jacqueline Kinghorn, Editors

SILVER EDITION CONSULTANTS

Fred Chavez, Director of Programs
Los Angeles City Reading Support Services Center
Los Angeles, California

Marguerite E. Fuller, Assistant Supervisor of Language Arts
Norwalk Public Schools
Norwalk, Connecticut

Sister Maria Loyola, I.H.M.,Chairperson, Reading Curriculum Committee
Archdiocese of Philadelphia
Philadelphia, Pennsylvania

Dr. John. F. Savage, Coordinator, Reading Specialist Program
Boston College, School of Education
Chestnut Hill, Massachusetts

Richard B. Solymos, Reading Resource Teacher
School Board of Broward County
Fort Lauderdale, Florida

READER'S DIGEST EDUCATIONAL DIVISION
© 1977 by Reader's Digest Services, Inc., Pleasantville, N.Y. 10570. All rights reserved, including
the right to reproduce this book or parts thereof in any form.
Printed in the United States of America.
Reader's Digest ® Trademark Reg. U.S. Pat. Off. Marca Registrada ISBN 0-88300-409-7

■ ■ **Part 3**   *Silver Edition*

STORIES

🔲 Stories for which Audio Lessons are available.
RDX number indicates RDX card for that story.

The Wrld of Dr. Seuss

by James Stewart-Gordon

There are Grinches on the backs of his chairs. Pictures of Snumms and Sneetches dot the walls of his home. He has a closet filled with 500 "thinking caps" which help him dream up his stories. Unusual? Maybe. But Dr. Seuss (soos) has pleased millions of readers with stories like *The Cat in the Hat* and *To Think That I Saw It on Mulberry Street.*

Some say that Dr. Seuss is a genius because he is so smart. He thinks up stories and new kinds of animals and

Key Words
genius
hatches
publisher

people. He even does his own drawings.
Once he was asked why he draws so
strangely. His answer—"Because I
don't know how to draw at all."

His high school art teacher would agree with him. She once told him, "You will never learn to draw, Theodor." But that was about 50 years ago. Dr. Seuss now finds that people love his artwork!

Dr. Seuss is a genius for a lot of reasons. He has made movies. He has worked in television, too. *How the Grinch Stole Christmas* has been seen on TV many times.

Sometimes Dr. Seuss gets an idea by accident. *Horton Hatches the Egg* was born by chance. One day Dr. Seuss was sitting by a window, drawing a tree. The wind blew a picture of an elephant onto his drawing. Suddenly it looked as if the elephant was in the tree. That gave him the idea of Horton the elephant sitting on an egg to keep it warm.

6

Not all his good stories happen by chance. Dr. Seuss works very hard. He had to write *How the Grinch Stole Christmas* in one week! Otherwise the publisher couldn't print the book.

What happens if Dr. Seuss is stuck for the right word to put in a story? Maybe he'll choose one of his caps. He will think awhile. Then if he still can't think of the word he wants, he makes up a new word, like Grinch or Three-Muffed Apfel Moose. Nothing stops a genius like Dr. Seuss.

BY DR. SEUSS *supporting details*

Check (✔) the names of two books written by Dr. Seuss.

_____ 1. *Peter Pan*
_____ 2. *Horton Hatches the Egg*
_____ 3. *How the Grinch Stole Christmas*
_____ 4. *Charlie Brown*

⚷ *12 • Best Score 2 • My Score _____*

THE WHOLE TRUTH *characterization*

Write 1 before the sentences that do not describe Dr. Seuss. Write 2 before the ones that do.

_____ His art teacher told him he would be a famous artist.

_____ He has a closet filled with thinking caps.

_____ Some of his ideas happen by accident.

_____ Even the chairs in his home have Seuss characters on them.

⚷ *87 • Best Score 4 • My Score _____*

8

GENIUS AT WORK   *author's purpose*

The author wrote, "Some say that Dr. Seuss is a genius." Check (✔) the four sentences below that show this is true.

_____ 1. He makes up new words.
_____ 2. He doesn't like to read.
_____ 3. He went to high school.
_____ 4. He likes hats.
_____ 5. He can write a whole book in one week if he has to.
_____ 6. He does his own artwork.
_____ 7. He thinks up lots of new ideas.
_____ 8. He has been in movies and television specials.

☞ *125 • Best Score 4 • My Score* _____
All Best Scores 10 • All My Scores _____

DR. SEUSS AND YOU   *evaluation*

Do you think Dr. Seuss should have made his drawings of animals and people look real? Why or why not? Do you think he is a good artist? Give reasons for your answer.

9

Key Words

U. S. Air Force
North Pole
scientists
satellite
radio

The Northern Lights

by Robert Gannon

"Welcome aboard, Mr. Gannon," smiled the U.S. Air Force pilot.

I was climbing into a special Air Force jet. The jet's job was to follow, study and take pictures of the Northern Lights. I am a writer. I was going to write a story about the lights.

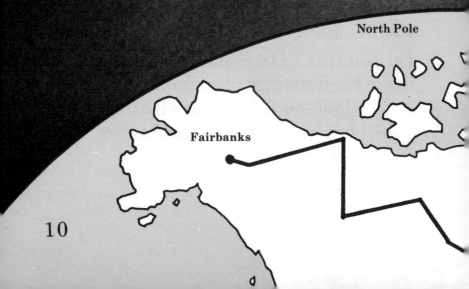

North Pole

Fairbanks

10

The Northern Lights are a beautiful show of lights in the dark sky. They are called the aurora borealis (uh-ROR-uh bor-ee-AHL-us). The aurora is caused by the sun. It is seen best at the North Pole.

I was going to study the Northern Lights from the sky. The Air Force plane would fly from Goose Bay, Labrador, to Fairbanks, Alaska. We would fly at a speed that would keep us in darkness during the whole flight. That way, we would be able to study the lights the entire time.

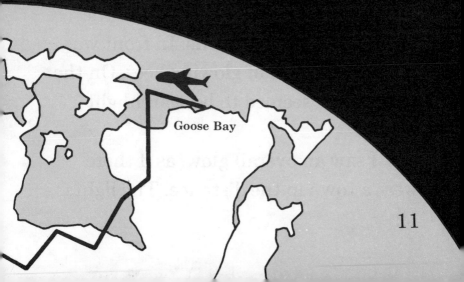

Goose Bay

On top of the jet was a TV camera. It was pointed up at the sky. What it saw would be flashed on the TV screen in our plane.

Sergeant James Smith turned the knobs on the TV screen. All at once, a streak of light swirled on the screen. Sergeant Smith yelled, "Look out the window!"

I rushed to the window. There was the aurora in all its beauty. The lights looked like strange shapes. Off to the left stood a row of swords. In front was a looping swarm of glowing bees. On the right, there seemed to be searchlight beams.

I saw an overall glow, as if there were a town in the distance. The lights

12

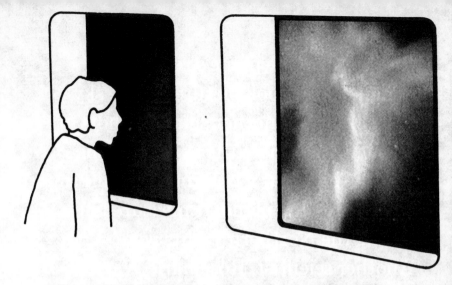

looked like smoke. The "smoke" became curls fluttering in the wind. I looked away for a minute. When I turned back, the lights seemed like curtains instead of curls.

"Each time we go up in a plane, the lights are different," said Dr. Whalen. He was one of the scientists on the plane. "But I don't think I've ever seen so much going on at one time."

A satellite came into view on the TV screen. The satellite was searching for information about the Northern Lights.

13

Set into the plane's roof were cameras. One took pictures of the sky each minute. Another snapped shots of the horizon (where the sky meets the land). There was a blinking machine in the back of the plane. It measured how strong the Northern Lights were. Another scientist, Rosemarie Wagner, was using a special machine to find out how high up the aurora was.

"These are just a few of our studies," Dr. Whalen told me. "There's

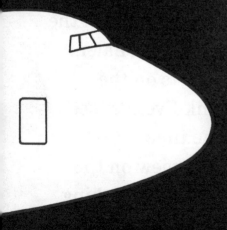

so much we do not know yet. The aurora can knock out electricity. It can stop shortwave radio messages from getting through. Maybe our studies will one day tell us when a radio blackout will happen."

I looked out the plane window once more. A snakelike band of light danced near the horizon. It seemed to be waving good-bye to me as we got ready to land.

A SPECIAL PLANE   *skimming*

Look back at the story. Check (✔) five things the scientists on the Air Force plane used to study the aurora.

_____ 1. X-rays
_____ 2. TV camera
_____ 3. sonar
_____ 4. cameras on top of the plane
_____ 5. satellite
_____ 6. machine to measure how high the lights are
_____ 7. telescope
_____ 8. TV screen

☞ *170 • Best Score 5 • My Score* _____

MR. GANNON'S REASONS   *author's purpose*

Check (✔) the two reasons Mr. Gannon went on the plane trip.

_____ 1. to learn about the Northern Lights
_____ 2. to take his first plane ride
_____ 3. to paint what he saw
_____ 4. to write about what he learned

☞ *22 • Best Score 2 • My Score* _____

16

BRILLIANT WORDS *figurative language*

The lights made the author think of things like smoke and curtains. In each blank, write the letter of the word or words that tell what the author was <u>really</u> seeing.

_____ Off to the left stood a row of swords.

_____ A snakelike band of light danced near the horizon.

_____ In front was a swarm of glowing bees.

   a. dots
   b. up-and-down lines
   c. a long, curved line

☞*52 • Best Score 3 • My Score* _____
All Best Scores 10 • All My Scores _____

A SKY FULL OF THINGS *opinion*

The sky has many beautiful things. It has the sun, the moon, clouds, rainbows and stars. Which one would you like to know more about? Why?

Key Words

kookaburra   Australia
Aborigine   slingshot
native   weapons

The Boy Who Shot the Kookaburra

by Kath Walker

I am an Aborigine (ab-uh-RIJ-uh-nee), a native of Australia. Today many Aborigines eat foods like beef and rice. They live in houses. They drive cars and watch television.

But the Aborigine way of life was different when my brothers and sisters and I were children. Our father never let us children forget we were natives of Australia.

He taught us how to catch our own food. We learned how to spear fish and

18

trap small animals. He gave us each a slingshot. We used them to bring down the parrots that lived in the trees.

There was one rule that he told us we could not break. Our weapons were to be used only for gathering food. We must never use them for the sake of killing. This is a law of the Aborigine. There is no excuse for breaking it.

One day five of us
children took our slingshots
to hunt for parrots. Our
oldest brother always bragged
about how well he could aim
his slingshot. So the rest of
us always let him have the
first shot.

This day he fired. And he missed!
Away flew the birds. They screeched as
they went.

Then we looked at our brother's
face. He was so surprised he had missed.
The rest of us roared with laughter at
him. Our other brother rolled over and
over, laughing his head off.

20

The more we all laughed, the angrier our oldest brother became. Then a kookaburra (kook-uh-BUR-uh) started to chuckle. The sound grew into a full laugh. It almost seemed as if the bird were laughing at our brother, too. In anger, our brother brought up his slingshot. He fired at the kookaburra.

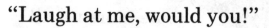

"Laugh at me, would you!"

Our laughter was cut short by the fall of the harmless bird. Our brother was shocked by what he had just done. We all stared at the poor creature.

Our brother's wild shot had broken the bird's wing. There was no way to fix it. The kookaburra would die if it couldn't fly to catch food or escape danger. And it was in pain.

We looked at one another in silence. He had harmed a bird we were not allowed to harm. The Aborigine does not eat the kookaburra. Its merry laughter brings the Aborigine happiness. It is our friend.

We did not see our father coming toward us. He must have been looking for firewood. When he came up to us, we stepped to one side to let him see what had happened.

Father held back his anger. He said nothing. He took a branch and killed the kookaburra to put the bird out of its pain.

I wished Father had spanked us. But I knew that was not his way. When we got home, Father told the five of us to go into the backyard. We had to bring our traps, slingshots and all our other weapons.

Father spoke for the first time since we had killed the kookaburra. He didn't ask for reasons for what we had done. We didn't offer any excuses.

All five of us took the blame. That is the way of the Aborigine. We had killed for the sake of killing. So for three months we couldn't hunt our own food. Instead we had to eat foods like rice and beef. They tasted <u>terrible</u> to us.

It happened a long time ago. But I still have dreams about it. The sad eyes of the kookaburra still haunt me.

SHOOT THE RIGHT PICTURE *vocabulary*
Circle the word that fits each picture.

1. Aborigine
2. American

1. America
2. Australia

1. spear
2. slingshot

1. turkey
2. kookaburra

87 • Best Score 4 • My Score _____

X OUT TWO *sequence*
Put an X in front of the two things that did <u>not</u> happen in the story.

_____ 1. The children went out to hunt.
_____ 2. The kookaburra flew away.
_____ 3. The oldest boy missed.
_____ 4. The children laughed at him.
_____ 5. The boy shot a kookaburra.
_____ 6. Their father spanked the boy.

39 • Best Score 2 • My Score _____

A GOOD FATHER *summary*

Check (✔) the four statements below that show how the writer's father helped her and her brothers and sisters.

_____ 1. He taught them how to do things for themselves.

_____ 2. He taught them to respect the Aborigine way of life.

_____ 3. He taught them how to read.

_____ 4. He knew a spanking was not always best for his children.

_____ 5. He trained them to do jobs that would bring them lots of money.

_____ 6. He taught them that living things were not to be killed without a good reason.

⚷ *123 • Best Score 4 • My Score* _____
All Best Scores 10 • All My Scores _____

WHO'S TO BLAME? *values*

Do you think it was fair that all the children in this story took the blame at the end? Why or why not?

Key Words   recording   mouthpiece
phonographs   recorded   violin
cylinder   records   jukebox

Those Wonderful Old-Time Music Machines

The child in the picture is standing next to a music box made in the 1800s. It was one of the earliest types of music machines for the home. Its tunes were made by a little metal cylinder studded with pins. As the cylinder turned, the pins hit a metal comb. Each time a pin struck a tooth of the comb, a musical note would come out.

28

by Cynthia A. Hoover

Radios, televisions, phonographs, tape players—all of these modern machines bring us music. But what did people use in the 1800s and early 1900s? The marvelous machines on the next few pages will give you an idea.

This is Thomas Edison's Speaking Phonograph. It was made in 1877. A person made a recording by speaking or singing into the mouthpiece. At the same time, he or she had to turn the handle. The sounds were recorded onto the metal cylinder. But they didn't sound much like the person's real voice.

Frances Denmore wanted to collect as many American Indian songs as she could. This man recorded such a song for her. He sang into the large horn. There was no way to make his voice sound louder. So it was up to him to sing loud enough for the machine to pick up his song. This was the way all recordings were made until 1925.

30

This is the Edison phonograph of 1907. A cylinder with a recording on it was put into place. The handle on the right was turned. Music or speech would pour out of the huge horn. The cabinet on which the phonograph sat could hold 100 cylinders. Thomas Edison thought cylinder phonographs were better than the ones that used flat, round records. So he went on making cylinder machines until 1929. By then most people had already switched to records.

◀ *Need a violin? A piano? You could have both in this handy, dandy Violano-Virtuoso. But you would have had to live anytime from 1910 until the 1920s.*

What do you think this machine is? It's a homemade radio! In the 1920s, lots of people put together their own. The simple one below could be built from pieces of wood, wires and an oatmeal box.

This was the machine that came before the jukebox. It held 24 cylinders. It was the first phonograph that played when coins were put in.

This 1946 jukebox brought people not only music but a bubbling light show as well. ►

WURLIZER

PUT IN THE RIGHT PART   *vocabulary*

Write the letters of the correct words in the blanks below.

1. Two kinds of old-time music-making machines were the _____ and the _____.
    a. music box   b. TV   c. jukebox

2. Thomas Edison made _____.
    a. phonographs   b. telephones
    c. cameras

3. His early recording machines used a handle, a _____ and a _____.
    a. battery   b. cylinder
    c. mouthpiece

4. The sound came out of a _____.
    a. speaker   b. horn   c. tape

⌐➤ *96 • Best Score 6 • My Score* _____

OLD AND NEW SOUNDS   *graphics*

The objects or actions pictured are used to make sounds <u>today</u>. In the box underneath are listed the things used to make the same sounds <u>in the old days</u>. Write the numeral of each group of words in the blank under the picture it matches.

Today

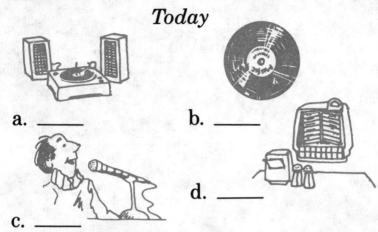

a. _____

b. _____

d. _____

c. _____

Yesterday
1. a phonograph
2. a cylinder
3. talking into a mouthpiece
4. a jukebox

104 • *Best Score 4* • *My Score* _____
All Best Scores 10 • *All My Scores* _____

GOOD OLD DAYS *comparison/contrast*

Do you have anything at home that is very old? Tell about it. Do people today have things that are like it?

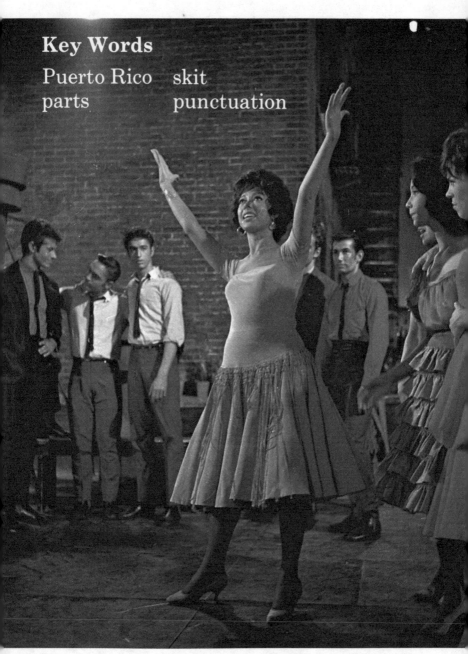

Key Words

Puerto Rico   skit
parts   punctuation

Rita Moreno in the Movie West Side Story.

Meet Rita Moreno

by Patricia Baum

Do you know the name Rita Moreno? Maybe you have seen her as Pandora, the brat in the TV show *The Electric Company*. Rita is famous for her acting, singing and dancing. She has been in movies, in plays and on TV.

Rita Moreno's real name is Rosita Dolores Alverio (ahl-VAYR-ee-oh). "My mother and I came to New York from Puerto Rico when I was only five," Rita remembers. "We were very poor. So we stayed in my aunt's apartment."

When Rita was only five years old, she was given singing and dancing jobs in her neighborhood. When she was 13, she did her first big show. She was in her first Hollywood movie when she was 17.

39

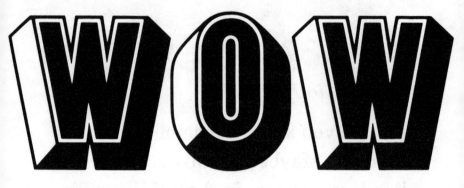

In these movies, Rita was always
asked to play the same kind of person.
At last she was asked to play Anita in
the movie *West Side Story*. She hoped
that people would see how good her
acting was and give her different kinds
of parts. But the movie parts stayed the
same.

So Rita tried TV and plays. And
that's the way she and *The Electric
Company* found each other. She got to
play lots of unusual characters. But the
show was more than just fun. It helped
children learn to read.

She did one skit on *The Electric Company* to teach punctuation. In the skit, Rita played the part of Pandora. She was very tiny on the screen. Behind her were huge letters that spelled *WOW*. There was a period (.) after the *WOW*. Pandora did a bad tap dance. You heard voices say a very weak "Wow."

She turned around to see what the problem was. She went to the word and

41

kicked off the period. Then she brought in an exclamation mark (!) and put it after the word. She danced again. This time she heard a big "WOW!"

Reading problems came right into Rita's own home. Her young daughter was having a hard time with reading in school. She learned to read from watching *The Electric Company*.

Rita's husband, Leonard, is a doctor in New York. They are good parents to their daughter, Nandy.

Rita and her husband have set up a set of rules that are loving but firm. "I let Nandy have fun, as long as it does no harm," says Rita. "But Nandy also has certain things she has to do.

"Even when I punish Nandy, I always tell her that I love her. I'll growl, 'I love you—but I can't stand you now!' I think that by laying down the rules and telling her I love her at

the same time, I show Nandy how much I care for her. I help her to like herself. By loving herself, she'll be able to love others."

Rita knows. She loves herself, her family and her work. And she is loved in return.

RITA'S CAREER   *supporting details*

Write the letter of the correct ending in each blank.

1. Rita was born in _____.
   a. Puerto Rico
   b. New York City
   c. Hollywood

2. Rita and her mother lived with her aunt because _____.
   a. they didn't have much money
   b. her aunt taught her to dance
   c. they couldn't find an apartment

3. Rita hated her early acting parts because _____.
   a. she really wanted to dance and sing
   b. they didn't pay her enough
   c. they were all the same

4. She got the parts she wanted after she _____.
   a. joined *The Electric Company*
   b. made her first movie
   c. was in *West Side Story*

☞ *92 • Best Score 4 • My Score* _____

44

DESCRIBE RITA   *characterization*

Put an X before the three statements
below that describe Rita Moreno.

_____ 1. She is a good actor and dancer.
_____ 2. Her job is more important than
            Nandy.
_____ 3. She lives with her aunt.
_____ 4. She writes for television.
_____ 5. People love her.
_____ 6. She is a firm but loving parent.

☞ 82 • Best Score 3 • My Score _____

PANDORA'S SKIT   *signals/antecedents*

Put 1 in the blank next to the *wow* with
the most feeling. Write 2 before the one
with less feeling and 3 before the one
with the least feeling.

_____ Wow.   _____ WOW.   _____ WOW!

☞ 54 • Best Score 3 • My Score _____
All Best Scores 10 • All My Scores _____

A CAREER FOR YOU   *self-awareness*

What career would you like? Why?

45

The Drama of a Drop

by Ed Burks

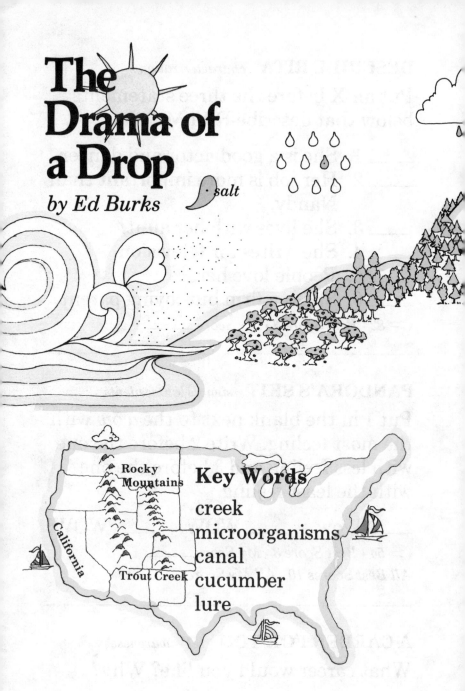

salt

Key Words

creek
microorganisms
canal
cucumber
lure

Rocky Mountains

California

Trout Creek

cloud

ice

snowflake

Rocky Mountains

The hot noonday sun blazed down on the California beach. A big wave threw its spray into the air. The sun dried up the spray.

Bits of salt left over from the sea spray were carried into the sky. Each bit of salt became the center of a tiny drop of water. Billions of these tiny drops formed a cloud.

The cloud rolled toward the Rocky Mountains. Another cloud formed above it. This new cloud dropped ice on the lower cloud. And so, snowflakes formed.

The snowflakes fell to earth. In this snow shower, the Drop was born. It was a Snowflake. It fell onto old snow.

47

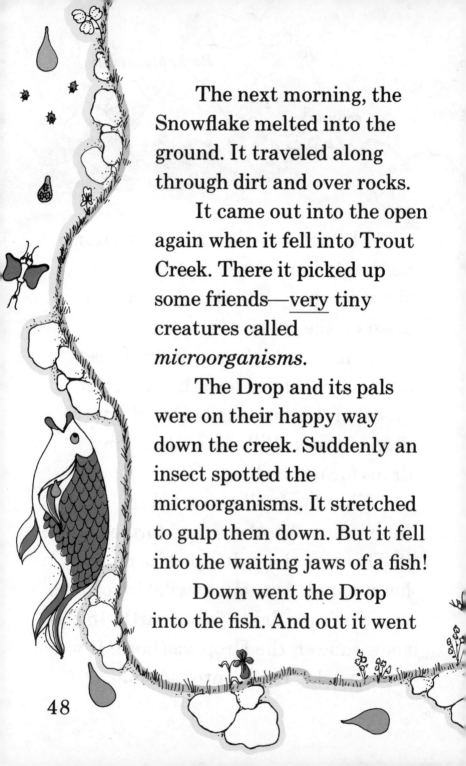

The next morning, the Snowflake melted into the ground. It traveled along through dirt and over rocks.

It came out into the open again when it fell into Trout Creek. There it picked up some friends—<u>very</u> tiny creatures called *microorganisms*.

The Drop and its pals were on their happy way down the creek. Suddenly an insect spotted the microorganisms. It stretched to gulp them down. But it fell into the waiting jaws of a fish!

Down went the Drop into the fish. And out it went

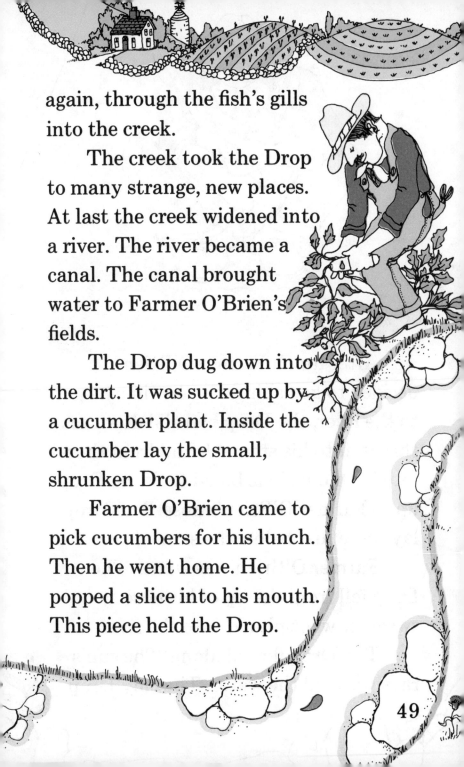

again, through the fish's gills into the creek.

The creek took the Drop to many strange, new places. At last the creek widened into a river. The river became a canal. The canal brought water to Farmer O'Brien's fields.

The Drop dug down into the dirt. It was sucked up by a cucumber plant. Inside the cucumber lay the small, shrunken Drop.

Farmer O'Brien came to pick cucumbers for his lunch. Then he went home. He popped a slice into his mouth. This piece held the Drop.

49

After lunch Farmer O'Brien decided to go fishing. By the time he got to the river, the Drop had slid down his throat, into his stomach and from there into his blood. The blood took the Drop up to Farmer O'Brien's nose. The Drop lay there just below the skin.

Farmer O'Brien was warm. The Drop fell from the tip of his nose as sweat. It went plunk! into the river.

The Drop flowed along. The sun's rays warmed the water. The tiny Drop

50

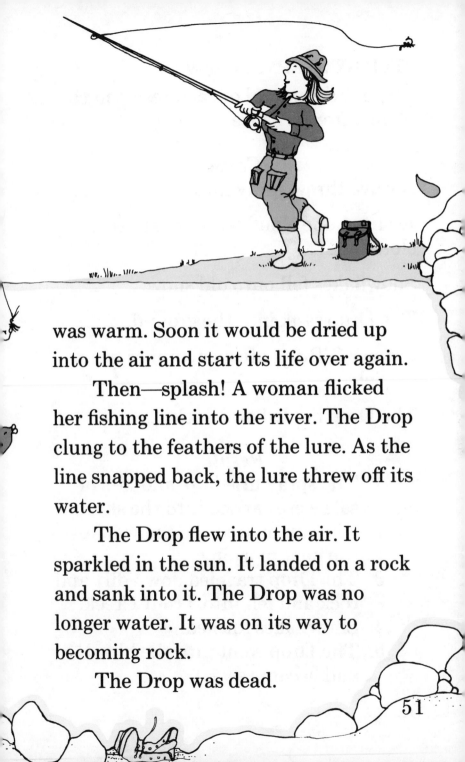

was warm. Soon it would be dried up into the air and start its life over again.

Then—splash! A woman flicked her fishing line into the river. The Drop clung to the feathers of the lure. As the line snapped back, the lure threw off its water.

The Drop flew into the air. It sparkled in the sun. It landed on a rock and sank into it. The Drop was no longer water. It was on its way to becoming rock.

The Drop was dead.

51

STEP BY STEP *cause/effect*

Write the numeral of each result in the
blank after its cause.

Cause

A wave threw spray into the air. _____

Ice from one cloud fell onto another
cloud. _____

Snowflakes fell onto old snow. _____

The Drop sank into the ground. _____

Farmer O'Brien ate a cucumber from
his field. _____

The Drop landed on a rock. _____

Result

1. The spray dried up, and bits of
   salt were carried into the sky.
2. The sun melted the Snowflake
   the next morning.
3. The Drop traveled down dirt and
   rock and fell into Trout Creek.
4. Snowflakes formed.
5. The Drop went into the blood
   and became sweat.

6. The Drop died.

☞ 212 • *Best Score 6* • *My Score* _____

LOOK IT UP *skimming*

Where would you look to find the answers to the following questions? Write A if you would look at the map on page 46 to find the answer. Write B if you would look at the pictures to find the answer. Write C if you would read the story to find the answer.

_____ How did the Drop become sweat?

_____ How many drops make one cloud?

_____ What did Farmer O'Brien look like?

_____ Where is Trout Creek?

☞ 91 • *Best Score 4* • *My Score* _____

All Best Scores 10 • *All My Scores* _____

THE END OF THE STORY? *sentence meaning*

What did the author mean when he wrote, "The Drop was dead"? Why did he say that? Do you think the Drop was dead? Explain.

Key Words

pedaled
bumper stickers

Bike Ride

by Millicent Haigwood

The Woods family was very busy.
It was moving day. That morning the
moving-van workers had brought boxes,
crates and furniture to the Woods' new
home. Now it was time for the Woods
to arrange the furniture and unpack.

Mrs. Woods looked around at the
jumble of things in the living room and
said, "Why don't we arrange the
upstairs rooms first?" Mr. and Mrs.
Woods each took one end of a big box.

Their daughter, Louise, asked, "Can
I help?"

54

Mr. Woods gasped,
"Can't you see we're busy right
now?" He was puffing from carrying
his end of the heavy box.

"But I just want to help. Maybe I
can help hold up this corner," Louise
said.

"Louise! Don't touch that!" cried
Mr. Woods. But his warning came too

55

late. Crash! Down banged the box on
his big toe. "OW!"

Louise didn't wait around. She
made a fast escape down the stairs,
hopped on her bike and rode off.

Louise pedaled as fast as she could.
Then, after a few minutes, she turned
back toward her new house.

She began to look at all the houses.
She noticed the cars parked in the

driveways. Something about one car interested her, and she stopped to study it.

Louise pedaled to the next driveway. She smiled. She did the same thing at almost every driveway on the way back to her house.

By the time Louise got home, dinner had been put on the table. Her parents were no longer angry at her. Louise quickly washed her hands and sat down at the table.

"I wonder what our neighbors are like?" Mrs. Woods was asking.

Mr. Woods said, "I was thinking that, too. We don't know anyone here."

"<u>Now</u> I can help," thought Louise. She spoke up. "It's not hard to make friends. You should talk to the people next door. You could play golf with them. And I could go bowling with the kids in the house across the street."

"Well, Louise, you didn't waste time meeting people," Mrs. Woods said.

"I didn't meet anyone. Don't you want to know about our other neighbors? The family on the corner has a child at State College. The family in the brown house went to Washington, D.C., and Yellowstone National Park. The family in the blue house has traveled to Japan and Mexico. The people in the little yellow house at the end of the street want to save whales and—"

Mr. Woods interrupted. "Wait a minute, Louise! You said you haven't even <u>met</u> our neighbors yet. How do you know so much about them?"

"When I drove around on my bike, I read everyone's bumper stickers."

INFORMATION, PLEASE   *story elements*

Match each detail with the important information. Write the letters in the blanks.

Details

a. answering important questions
b. the Woods' new neighborhood
c. Mr. and Mrs. Woods and Louise
d. gets into trouble whenever she tries to help

Important Information

The story happens in _____.
The names of the people are _____.
Louise's problem is that she _____.
Louise solved her problem by _____.

🗝 *103 • Best Score 4 • My Score* _____

THE WOODS FAMILY   *points of view*

Who would have said the things below? Write the numerals in the blanks.

1. Mr. Woods   3. Mr. and Mrs. Woods
2. Mrs. Woods   4. Louise

_____ "I just want to help."
_____ "How do we make new friends?"

_____ "This box is too heavy for me."
_____ "Let's arrange this room first."
🔑 105 • *Best Score 4* • *My Score* _____

MOVE IN ON THE IDEAS *main idea*

Check (✔) the two most important ideas in the story.

_____ 1. Moving is hard work.
_____ 2. People should ride bikes.
_____ 3. Japan and Mexico are two interesting countries to visit.
_____ 4. People can learn a lot by noticing things around them.
_____ 5. Children shouldn't lift boxes.
_____ 6. Making new friends may not be as hard as some people think.

🔑 40 • *Best Score 2* • *My Score* _____
All Best Scores 10 • *All My Scores* _____

BUMPER STICKER *summary*

If you were to choose a bumper sticker, what would it say? What would it tell other people about you?

Princes of Laughter

by Robert M. Hill

Long ago there
were kings, queens
and knights. There was
also another very special
kind of person—the royal jester.

He lived in the castle of the king or
queen. His job was like the clown's job
today. He made people laugh.

62

The royal jester had a quick mind. But he could <u>pretend</u> to be a fool. Another word for a jester was "fool." "The king's fool" meant "the king's jester." His silly actions would make the people in the castle feel much smarter.

Castles were damp. They were also dark and smoky, for they were lit only by firelight and a little daylight. The jester had to think of interesting things to talk about. His words brought life to the gloom of the castles.

The jester could think of lots of ways to entertain the king or queen. He also knew better than to go too far with his jokes. He was smart.

Kings and queens liked lots of bright colors. So the fool wore a colorful outfit. Yellow was the fool's color.

The jester was one of the king or queen's favorite people. He was like a prince in some ways. The jester could roam through the castle. He could say almost anything he wished.

But times changed. Printing presses made books cheap to buy. The theater came into being. The jester began to be less and less useful. Books and actors entertained people.

Other changes were happening. Castles no longer shut people off from the rest of the world. Many people moved into towns and cities. There were lots of things to do there.

Most people no longer needed kings and queens to rule over them. Many castles were left empty. There were no longer places for the jesters to work and live.

In 1728 a jester named Dicky Pearce died. He was one of the last jesters of England. With him ended the long line of jesters who had been part of castle life for at least 700 years.

JESTER'S TRUE COLORS *supporting details*

Check (✔) the three statements that tell what a jester had to do.

The royal jester had to . . .

_____ 1. fight for the king or queen.

_____ 2. be smart.

_____ 3. teach others how to be jesters.

_____ 4. talk about interesting things.

_____ 5. be a prince.

_____ 6. be funny.

🔑 *83 • Best Score 3 • My Score* _____

THE JESTER'S RISE AND FALL *sequence*

Put the sentences below into the correct order. The second one has been filled in for you. Put 1 before the thing that happened first, 3 before what happened third and 4 before what happened last.

_____ Dicky Pearce died in 1728.

_____ Many castles were left empty.

_____ The jester entertained the people in the castle.

__2__ People began moving to cities.

🔑 *105 • Best Score 3 • My Score* _____

FUNNY PEOPLE   *comparison/contrast*

Write 1 if the sentence is true of jesters,
2 if true of clowns and 3 if true of both
jesters and clowns.

_____ They make people laugh.
_____ They lived in castles.
_____ They work for the circus.
_____ They wear colorful clothes.

⚷ 95 · Best Score 4 · My Score _____
All Best Scores 10 · All My Scores _____

THAT'S ENTERTAINMENT   *opinion*

Why were jesters no longer used to
entertain people? Name some things
that entertain people today. Would you
rather have those things or a jester
entertain you? Explain.

A Gift from the Trees

by Roslyn W. Salny

Key Words

collect, collection
deciduous
evergreen
cones
blotters
scrapbook

Deciduous

Evergreen

Simple Leaf—
one leaf attached to stem

Needles

Compound Leaf—
several smaller leaves
attached to stem

Cone

68

What hobby lets you collect things that are both green and beautiful? Leaf collecting, of course. There are two main groups of trees. Deciduous trees drop all their leaves in the fall. Evergreens sometimes drop their needles and cones. But they stay green all year.

A good leaf collection should show leaves in different ways. It should show both sides of the leaf. Collect leaves with pretty fall colors, too.

Tools

Scissors help cut the leaf from the tree.

A magnifying glass gives you a close look at the leaf.

A field manual has pictures of trees, leaves and cones. It will help you learn their names.

Gathering Leaves

1. Cut from the lowest branches.

2. Take the whole leaf, including its stem. Use your scissors and don't hurt the tree by breaking off a branch.

3. Take only a few leaves from any one tree.

4. Collect green leaves in the spring, before insects and storms harm them.

5. Gather fall leaves as soon as they turn color.

Drying the Leaf

Now you have to bring your leaf home. Put it in a plastic bag or an airtight box. When you get home, you have to dry out the leaf.

70

Pressing is the usual way. Place the leaf between two blotters. Put this "sandwich" between some sheets of newspaper. Next put a flat, heavy weight on top. Change the blotters and paper each day or two until the leaf becomes hard and dry.

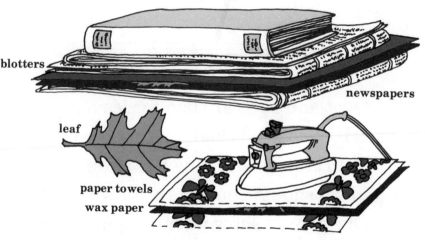

There is another way to dry a leaf. Put it between sheets of wax paper. Put paper towels underneath and on top. Get an adult to press it with a warm (not a hot) iron. The wax on the paper will melt. It will put a thin coating on the leaf. This will protect the leaf.

71

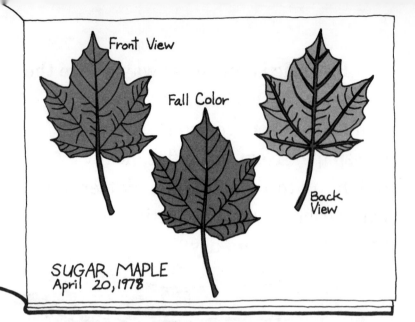

Front View

Fall Color

Back View

SUGAR MAPLE
April 20, 1978

Saving Your Leaves

Dust and light are bad for leaves, so it is best to keep them in a scrapbook.

Put three of the same leaves on a page. Two should show both sides of the leaf. One should show its fall color.

How do you hold them in place? Use glue that can't be seen when dry. Or use tape that is sticky on both sides.

Keep track of your collection. Put information in one corner of the page. List the name of each leaf. Write down the date you found it.

72

Collecting Cones

Cones are hard leaves that protect seeds inside. Pick up cones that have fallen to the ground. Wash them in soap and water to get off the sticky stuff on the outside. Dry them outdoors or near heat. Then spray them with a clear plastic spray. (Follow the directions on the can.)

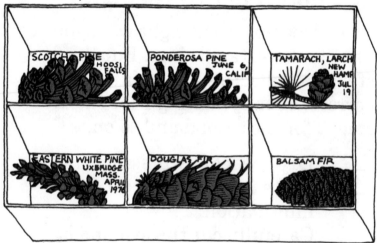

You can keep your cone collection in a bookcase or in shoe boxes. Put in a card with the following information— the name of the tree and the place and date the cone was collected.

TOOLS OF THE TRADE   *supporting details*

Which two items listed below would you not need if you were a leaf and cone collector? Circle the numerals.

1. field manual   4. paint
2. scrapbook   5. scissors
3. plastic spray   6. paper clips

⚷ *40 • Best Score 2 • My Score* _____

BE A GOOD COLLECTOR   *sequence*

To collect leaves the right way, you have to do certain things. Put the five steps for collecting leaves into the correct order by writing 1 for the first step, 2 for the second and so on.

_____ Dry the leaf by pressing.
_____ Write down the important information.
_____ Carefully cut the leaf and its stem from the tree or plant.
_____ Put the leaf into a box or bag.
_____ Put the leaf in your scrapbook.

⚷ *164 • Best Score 5 • My Score* _____

WHAT IS SHE SAYING? *author's purpose*

What three things was writer Roslyn
W. Salny trying to do in this story?
Check (✔) those three sentences.

Ms. Salny wanted to . . .

_____ a. teach you a little about leaves.
_____ b. help you grow your own trees.
_____ c. teach you how to begin a leaf
        collection.
_____ d. get you interested in becoming
        a forest ranger.
_____ e. share with you her love of
        leaves.

🗝 *74 • Best Score 3 • My Score* _____
All Best Scores 10 • All My Scores _____

WATCH THE TREES *classification/outline*

What time of the year do deciduous
trees drop their leaves? When do these
trees grow new, green leaves? Which
time of year do you think the trees in
your part of the country look prettiest?
Why?

Key Words
Switzerland
chamois
canyon
Alps
76

In Search of the Shy Chamois

by Emily and Ola d'Aulaire

We climbed up the steep mountain path. Sky, rocks and trees all seemed gray in the early morning light. We were in Switzerland. We had come to see an animal called the chamois (SHAM-ee).

At last we reached a rocky field. Suddenly we saw seven chamois. Their beautiful, thin, small horns went straight up and then ended in tiny hooks. Black stripes went down from their ears to their noses. Their red-brown coats shone in the sun.

The chamois have learned to breathe the thin mountain air with no trouble at all. They can hear, smell and see extremely well.

In deep winter, the chamois moves down into the forests. During the rest of the year, it lives high up in the mountains. The chamois can leap across a canyon 23 feet (7 meters) wide. It can jump lightly from a cliff three stories high.

The animal's feet and legs are made for this kind of action. The chamois has a hoof with two toes. On snow the webbed toes spread apart. In that way, the chamois does not sink into the snow. The hoof is pointed in

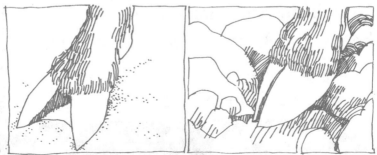

front. When going up a hill, the point digs into small cracks.

A baby chamois can use its feet and legs soon after it is born. After just a few hours, it runs so fast that no one can catch it.

In the Alps, hunters used to kill thousands of chamois for their meat, horns and skin. The soft skin was used for cleaning glass, silver and cars.

The chamois is still hunted. But now laws protect it. Only a certain number of chamois can be shot each year. So the swift, shy chamois is still safe in its rocky world, high among the cliffs.

CHAMOIS FACTS *classification/outline*

Facts about the chamois are listed below. Write A if the sentence tells how the chamois <u>acts</u> and B if it tells how it <u>looks</u>.

_____ It can jump lightly from a cliff three stories high.

_____ Its hoof is pointed in front.

_____ After just a few hours, a baby chamois runs so fast that no one can catch it.

_____ Its beautiful, thin, small horns go straight up and end in hooks.

⌐ *84 • Best Score 4 • My Score* _____

STAYING ALIVE *inferences*

Check (✔) the four things that help the chamois stay alive in the mountains.

The chamois . . .

_____ 1. has good hearing, smell and eyesight to warn of danger.

_____ 2. can breathe thin air.

_____ 3. has a skin that can be used for cleaning things.

_____ 4. doesn't sink in snow.

_____ 5. lives all over the world.

_____ 6. can walk on icy hillsides.

☞ 123 • *Best Score 4* • *My Score* _____

WHAT ABOUT THE CHAMOIS? *summary*

Check (✔) the two best titles that sum up the main ideas in the story.

_____ 1. "The Animals of Switzerland"

_____ 2. "Our Swiss Guide"

_____ 3. "The Chamois—Beautiful and Swift"

_____ 4. "At Home on Cliffs and Snow"

☞ 24 • *Best Score 2* • *My Score* _____

All Best Scores 10 • *All My Scores* _____

IN THE ALPS *paragraph meaning*

Read the last two paragraphs on page 79. Why did hunters try to kill the chamois? Why did Switzerland pass laws to protect the animal? Do you think the writers want to see the chamois hunted or protected? Give reasons for your answer.

The Possible Dream

by Alain de Penanster

At first it was just a dream, an idea. Finally he made it come true. Joseph-Ferdinand Cheval (shuh-VAHL) spent 33 years building his "Perfect Palace."

The "Perfect Palace" stands in a farmer's field in France. The building itself is quite a surprise. It doesn't look like a farm building. It looks like a very strange castle.

It has many different shapes and bright colors. Twisting towers and hidden steps make the palace mysterious. Joseph had pictures of animals cut into one of the castle's rock walls. There is even a stone zoo.

Key Words

palace
France
mysterious
daydream

83

How did Joseph build his dream? He was a mail carrier in a village in France. He used to daydream while he was carrying mail to homes and farms. He would dream about a fairy castle. One day his foot struck a strange looking rock. He picked up the rock and took it home. The next day he saw another odd rock.

Each day, Joseph would look for unusual stones on the ground. He would heap them in piles along the road. Later he would come with a wheelbarrow and take his rocks home. He saved his favorite stones for building the palace.

Soon he was working day and night on his castle. People in his village thought he was out of his mind. He slept just five hours a night. He had dinner brought to him each evening. He worked until he went to bed.

Joseph slowly built his palace. He used only materials found in nature. He made caves, a waterfall and six staircases. He even made a building called the Washington White House.

At last Joseph finished. He had worked from 1879 to 1912—33 years!

Then Joseph opened his "Perfect Palace" for everyone to visit. Today people from all over the world visit the palace each year. Joseph had made his dream come true.

IMPORTANT WORDS *phrase meaning*

In each blank below, fill in the numeral of the phrase that best completes the sentence.

1. in a farmer's field
2. along the road
3. with a wheelbarrow

The castle stands _____ in France.
Joseph heaped the stones in piles _____.
Later he would come back _____ and take his rocks home.

⚷ *55 • Best Score 3 • My Score* _____

BUILDING A PALACE *supporting details*

Check (✔) the three correct endings for the sentence below.

The "Perfect Palace" is different from most buildings because it . . .
_____ 1. was built very quickly.
_____ 2. has many kinds of shapes.
_____ 3. has trees around it.
_____ 4. is made of rocks picked up along the road.

_____ 5. was built by a mail carrier.

☞ 77 • *Best Score 3* • *My Score* _____

MR. CHEVAL   *characterization*

What sort of person do you think
Joseph-Ferdinand Cheval was? Check
(✔) the four statements below that
would seem to be true of him, based on
the things the writer told you.

_____ 1. He loved France.
_____ 2. He came up with ideas.
_____ 3. He worked hard.
_____ 4. He was a good mail carrier.
_____ 5. He made use of the things
          around him.
_____ 6. He was proud of his work.

☞ 122 • *Best Score 4* • *My Score* _____
All Best Scores 10 • *All My Scores* _____

A DREAM COME TRUE   *comparison/contrast*

Joseph worked to make his dream come
true. Have you done or made something
that took a long time or was hard to do?
Tell about it.

Key Words

grizzly
cubs
forest ranger
artist

Four Legs and a Bunch of Claws

by David Wynne

"We're not going to see this bear tonight," Betty Vroom said softly. She pointed to five deep holes where sharp bear claws had dug into the dirt.

"This grizzly bear is young," she explained. "It knows there's a mother bear that feeds her cubs here at night. A mother bear can become very mean when she's got cubs to feed. So the young bear is moving on."

88

I knew Betty was right. She was a forest ranger. So she had to know almost everything about the woods and all the animals living there.

I am an artist. I was going to buy a big block of black stone. I wanted to cut away at it until it looked like a big, black, silent bear. So I had come to the wilds of Banff National Park to study them.

The park ranger and I had been looking for a bear for a week. The body of a deer lay on the side of a hill. Bear footprints told Betty that the mother bear had killed the deer. The deer meat would be food for her and her cubs.

We waited for the bears by a tree at the bottom of the hill. The moon rose. A wolf howled. Other wolves answered. But no bears came.

Then I looked up. Side by side, four bears came over the hill. Their fur was a lovely gold and brown.

The mother bear rose up on her back legs and whoofed and snorted. She was nervous about us. She wasn't sure if we were going to harm her three cubs.

Her cubs didn't mind us. One shoved his nose into the deer meat. The others scratched and rolled about. I grabbed my camera and clicked away.

For two mornings and two nights, Betty and I watched this bear family. The mother would never eat when we were there. But she would play with the cubs in the grass.

90

On our last night, there was no
noise but the barking of a coyote. Then
suddenly the bears came from behind
us! The mother stood tall. She snarled
and growled. Betty looked at the gun
she kept by her side.

"The mother grizzly is mad
because we're between the cubs and the
deer meat," Betty said quietly.

The cubs kept coming closer to us. The mother was getting madder. My camera clicked away as she snarled and clawed the air.

She began to lead her cubs up the hill. But the young bears left her and ran right to us!

With a roar, the mother began running toward me. Her mouth was open. I saw four legs and a bunch of claws through my camera.

Betty aimed her gun at the mother. I thought, "No, Betty. Don't kill her! The cubs need their mother. They'll die!"

But Betty didn't fire. She stepped in front of the bear and waved an arm. She shouted, "Get away!"

I couldn't believe it! The grizzly skidded to a stop. Growling and scolding, she turned to the cubs. Then she led them up the hill. They followed quietly.

Betty said, "There aren't many grizzly bears left. If we kill them, we kill these wilds, these woods and mountains.

"I have read that sometimes you can stop a wild horse by scaring it. I had a few seconds before I had to fire at the bear. She was worth a try."

WHAT IS IT? *classification/outline*

Write A if the item is an object, B if it's an animal and C if it's a part of an animal's body.

_____ 1. camera   _____ 4. fur
_____ 2. grizzly   _____ 5. gun
_____ 3. claws

133 • Best Score 5 • My Score _____

THE BEAR FACTS *generalizations*

Draw a line under the two things about bears that you learned from the story.

1. Bears can't run very fast.

2. Mother bears protect their cubs.

3. Bears only come out at night.

4. Mother bears are very friendly when they have cubs.

5. Grizzly bears are short, even when they stand up.

6. Bear cubs need both food and love from their mother if they are to live.

39 • Best Score 2 • My Score _____

READ THE FOOTPRINTS   *main idea*

Check (✔) the three sentences below that tell you the <u>most important</u> ideas in "Four Legs and a Bunch of Claws."

_____ 1. The mother bear had three cubs.

_____ 2. The grizzly is a wild, beautiful animal.

_____ 3. Grizzly bears aren't very dangerous.

_____ 4. Children in the future have a right to be able to see bears and other animals in the wild.

_____ 5. Betty Vroom is a park ranger.

_____ 6. It's a shame to kill grizzlies and other animals, because they are an important part of the forest.

☞ 83 • Best Score 3 • My Score _____
All Best Scores 10 • All My Scores _____

WILD ANIMALS   *comparison/contrast*

Wild animals find their own food. Pets don't have to. What are some other things wild animals do that are different from what pets do?

345ADW7654321O9